ANSWER LINK
QUIZZES

First published in 2002 by Miles Kelly Publishing Ltd,
Bardfield Centre, Great Bardfield, Essex, CM7 4SL

Copyright © Miles Kelly Publishing Ltd 2002

This edition printed 2002

ISBN 1-84236-130-9

2 4 6 8 10 9 7 5 3

Project Manager: Ian Paulyn
Assistant: Lisa Clayden
Design: Clare Sleven

Contact us by email: info@mileskelly.net
Website: www.mileskelly.net

Printed in India

ANSWER LINK QUIZZES

by
Christopher Rigby

Miles Kelly
PUBLISHING

About the Author

Born in Blackburn, Lancashire in 1960, Christopher Rigby
has been compiling and presenting pub quizzes for the past
15 years. When he is not adding to his material for quizzes,
Christopher works in the car industry. He is married to
Clare – they have two teenage daughters, Hollie and Ashley
and share their home with two demented dogs called Vespa
and Bailey. A keen Manchester United fan Christopher lists
his heroes as George Best and Homer Simpson.

ANSWER LINKS EXPLAINED

The following quiz book comprises nine separate sessions of ten answer link quizzes of varying difficulty. Here's an example:

ANSWER LINKS: COUNTRIES
The answers to the following questions all contain the name of a country.

1. Matt Monro sang the theme for which James Bond film? (From RUSSIA With Love)
2. Which drinks company employed the advertising slogan "The Champagne of ginger ales"? (CANADA Dry)
3. Which song was a No.1 hit for T'Pau in 1987? (CHINA In Your Hand)
4. Who founded the Samaritans? (CHAD Varah)

COME ON YOU REDS!

....

The answers to the following ten questions all contain the word red.

1. What is the most common name for British pubs?
2. Which song reached No. 1 in the hit parade for the Rolling Stones in November 1964?
3. Which athlete did Sharron Davies divorce in 2000?
4. In which 1985 film was Tom Hanks mistaken for a spy because he had lost an item of footwear?
5. Which pop group was originally called the Frantic Elevators?
6. What is the name of the Muslim equivalent of the Red Cross?
7. In which TV drama did Sarah Lancashire play Coral Atkins?
8. What was the title of the 1984 film which starred a young Patrick Swayze as the leader of a gang of rebels fighting against a Russian invasion of America?
9. What did Paul Neal change his name to when he took up firefighting?
10. Which novel by Stephen Crane was set during the American Civil War?

ANSWERS

1. RED Lion 2. 'Little RED Rooster' 3. Derek REDmond 4. The Man With One RED Shoe 5. Simply RED 6. The RED Crescent 7. Seeing RED 8. RED Dawn 9. RED Adair 10. The RED Badge of Courage

PETER, PAUL AND MARY

The answers to the following ten questions all contain the names of Peter, Paul or Mary.

1. The opening line of which novel is 'All children grow up, except one'?

2. Who is the actress mother of Larry Hagman?

3. What was the name of the football referee infamously shoved to the ground by Paulo do Canio?

4. Who founded the National Viewers and Listeners Association in 1965?

5. In January 2001, it was announced that which pop superstar had become pop music's first billionaire?

6. In 1990 who became the Irish Republic's first female president?

7. Which TV programme celebrated its 35th birthday in September 1993?

8. Who won the most Wimbledon Men's Singles titles during the 20th Century?

9. In the Oscar-winning film *Ordinary People*, who played the wife of Donald Sutherland?

10. Who sang the first line in the original 'Feed the World' charity single by Band Aid?

ANSWERS

1. PETER *Pan* 2. MARY Martin 3. PAUL Alcock 4. MARY Whitehouse 5. PAUL McCartney 6. MARY Robinson 7. Blue PETER 8. PETE Sampras 9. MARY Tyler Moore 10. PAUL Young

BIRDS OF A FEATHER

The answers to the following ten questions all contain the name of a bird.

1. What is the alternative name for a castle in chess?
2. In Disney's *Aladdin* who provided the voice of the Genie?
3. What was the name of the organisation which was the arch enemy of the Men from UNCLE?
4. What was the title of the trilogy of novels written by Flora Thompson?
5. Which former England goalkeeper died in the Munich air crash whilst working as a newspaper reporter?
6. What was the alternative name of Sir Francis Drake's flagship *The Golden Hind*?
7. What was the name of the character played by Jodie Foster in *The Silence of the Lambs*?
8. Who had hit records with 'Splish Splash', 'Volare' and 'My Boomerang Won't Come Back'?
9. Which novel by Ken Kesey was set in a mental institution?
10. In *Star Wars* what was the name of Han Solo's spaceship?

ELEMENTARY

The answers to the following ten questions all contain the name of an element in the periodic table.

1. What was the name of the horse of the Lone Ranger?

2. Which TV competition presented by Gordon Burns featured the dreaded assault course?

3. Who was born Frederick Bulsara?

4. What are the two main constituents of bronze?

5. Which villain was portrayed on the big screen by Gert Frobe in 1964?

6. What puts the fizz in fizzy drinks?

7. What were the first five words of the No. 1 hit 'I Don't Like Mondays'?

8. Which co-presenter of the children's TV programme *Playaway* went on to win an Oscar for his portrayal of Claus Von Bulow?

9. Which heroic screen canine died in the arms of Jean Harlow?

10. What nickname was bestowed upon the island of Iwo Jima?

A PACK OF BROWNIES!

The answers to the following ten questions all contain the word brown.

1. What name is given to the leader of a Brownie pack?
2. Which song was on the flip side of the Boney M hit 'The Rivers of Babylon'?
3. Who presented the Budget in Tony Blair's first cabinet?
4. What nickname was given to the boxer Joe Louis?
5. Which fellow pop star married Whitney Houston?
6. Which novel featured a bully called Flashman?
7. Which GK Chesterton literary creation was played on TV by Kenneth More?
8. What did the DB stand for in the Aston Martin DB range of models?
9. Which song gave the Stranglers a No 2 hit in the new year of 1982?
10. What was the name of the gang leader in the Graham Greene novel *Brighton Rock*?

CITIES AROUND THE WORLD

The answers to the following ten questions all contain the name of a city.

1. Antonio was the title character in which Shakespeare play?

2. Which pop group had a No. 1 hit in 1986 with the song 'Take My Breath Away'?

3. In Dallas who played Pam Ewing?

4. Who featured on the back of the £5 note directly before Sir George Stephenson?

5. Who had a No. 3 hit in 1978 with an instrumental version of 'Annie's Song' originally a hit for John Denver?

6. What was the name of the feline companion of Mr Rigsby in *Rising Damp*?

7. Which Premiership footballer broke his neck in 1999 and played in the FA Cup Final in the year 2000?

8. Which song contains the line 'Have you seen the old man in the closed down market kicking up the papers with his worn out shoes?'

9. What was the name of the character played by Penelope Keith in the sitcom *To The Manor Born*?

10. Which object four metres (14 feet) in length and one metre (3.5 feet) wide is located in the cathedral of San Giovanni Battista and has been the subject of much conjecture?

ANSWERS

1. *The Merchant of VENICE* 2. BERLIN 3. VICTORIA Principle 4. The Duke of WELLINGTON 5. James GALWAY 6. Vienna 7. Dion DUBLIN 8. The Streets of LONDON 9. Audrey Forbes-HAMILTON 10. The TURIN shroud

DEAL ME IN

....

**The answers to the following ten questions all contain a
word that is associated with a deck of cards.**

1. What sank in 1972 after a fire in Hong Kong harbour?

2. In the 1970s which brand of beer used the advertising slogan 'It
   works wonders'?

3. The video for which Wham song featured George Michael lying
   in a swimming pool sipping a cocktail?

4. Which actor played a hieroglyphics expert in the film *Stargate*?

5. Whose daughters were called Regan, Goneril and Cordelia?

6. What name is given to a score of forty-all in tennis?

7. Who did the actor Sam Neill portray in a 1983 TV series?

8. Who wrote the novel *The Call of the Wild*?

9. Which song reached No 1 in 1990 for the Steve Miller Band
   after it had been used in a TV advertisement for Levi jeans?

10. The Vietnam War film *Apocalypse Now* was based on which Joseph
    Conrad novel?

ANSWERS
1. The QUEEN Elizabeth liner. 2. Double DIAMOND 3. CLUB Tropicana.
4. James SPADEr. 5. KING Lear. 6. DEUCE 7. Reilly ACE of Spies 8. JACK London
9. The JOKER. 10. HEART of Darkness

TEN BOB

The answers to the following ten questions all contain the name Bob or Bobby.

1. Who has presented the TV game shows *Call My Bluff* and *Blockbusters*?

2. Who killed Jesse James?

3. Who partnered Spit the Dog on TV?

4. What was the name of the clerk employed by Ebenezer Scrooge?

5. How is Robert Harper better known in the world of show business?

6. What was the name of the dog that became famous for watching over its master's grave for 14 years?

7. Which legendary pop star died on 11th May 1981 aged just 36?

8. Who was the first man to present the TV game show *Family Fortunes*?

9. Who wrote a book called *Confessions of a Hooker*?

10. In the 1950s children's TV programme there was a hedgehog called Rag, a mouse called Tag and a rabbit called –?

ANSWERS

1. BOB Holness 2. BOB Ford 3. BOB Carolgees 4. BOB Cratchit 5. BOBBY Ball 6. Greyfriars BOBBY 7. BOB Marley 8. BOB Monkhouse 9. BOB HOPE 10. BOBtail

SAY IT WITH FLOWERS

The answers to the following ten questions all contain the name of a flower.

1. Who does Patricia Routledge play in *Keeping Up Appearances*?

2. Why is the common name of Myosotis easy to remember?

3. Which song provided the Foundations with a No. 2 hit in 1968?

4. Which novel by Umberto Eco told the story of a priest who was also a medieval detective?

5. What is the name of Donald Duck's girlfriend?

6. In 1993 which pop group had a No. 1 hit with the song 'Young at Heart'?

7. In the year 2000 which model did Paul McCartney introduce as his new girlfriend?

8. In *Coronation Street* who for many years played the character of Ena Sharples?

9. Which famous racehorse won the Cheltenham Gold Cup in 1989?

10. In Greek mythology who was the goddess of the rainbow?

ANSWERS

1. HYACINTH Bucket 2. FORGET-ME-NOT 3. 'Build Me Up BUTTERCUP' 4. *The Name of the ROSE* 5. DAISY Duck 6. The BLUEBELLS 7. HEATHER Mills 8. VIOLET Carson 9. Desert ORCHID 10. IRIS

RAINING CATS AND DOGS

The answers to the following ten questions all contain the name, breed or species of cat or dog.

1. Which famous novel is set in the land of Narnia?
2. What was the name of Charles Darwin's research ship?
3. In the 1970s TV series of *Tarzan* what name was given to Tarzan's chimpanzee companion?
4. Which female pop group had hits with 'Automatic', 'Slowhand' and 'I'm So Excited'?
5. What is the nickname of Hull City FC?
6. Who is the patron saint of mountaineers?
7. What would an Iranian have been called before 1936?
8. Which American pop group had hits with 'Africa' and 'Roseanna'?
9. Two Oriental gentlemen by the name of Chang and Eng were the first recorded cases of what?
10. The Cabot Straits separates Nova Scotia from where?

ANSWERS

1. *The LION, the Witch and the Wardrobe* 2. HMS *BEAGLE* 3. CHEETAH 4. POINTER Sisters 5. The TIGERS 6. SAINT BERNARD 7. PERSIAN 8. TOTO (Dorothy's dog in *The Wizard of Oz*) 9. SIAMESE twins 10. NEWFOUNDLAND

BLACK OR WHITE

The answers to the following ten questions all contain the colour black or white.

1. Which comedy series features a manservant called Baldrick?
2. In the 1982 World Cup which 17-year-old Irish man became the youngest ever player to appear in the World Cup finals?
3. Which duo charted the song 'Agadoo'?
4. How is 1600 Pennsylvania Avenue better known?
5. Who shared a home with Ginger and Merrylegs?
6. Which song by Grandmaster Flash and Melle Mel advised against the perils of snorting cocaine?
7. The Nawab of Bengal was responsible for establishing which infamous prison in India?
8. In which film did James Cagney play gang-leader Cody Jarrett?
9. Which rock group led by Ozzy Osbourne took their name from a Dennis Wheatley novel?
10. In which song did Procul Harem sing about sixteen vestal virgins?

ANSWERS

1. BLACKAdder 2. Norman WHITEside 3. BLACK Lace 4. The WHITE House 5. BLACK Beauty 6. WHITE Lines Don't Do It' 7. The BLACK Hole of Calcutta 8. WHITE Heat 9. BLACK Sabbath 10. 'A WHITER Shade of Pale'

TOM, DICK AND HARRY

The answers to the following ten questions all contain the name Tom, Dick or Harry.

1. What was the character name of the police detective who appeared in the films *Sudden Impact* and *The Enforcer*?

2. Which former jockey wrote the novel *Dead Cert*?

3. Who was the famous manager of Elvis Presley?

4. Which was the first ever company to issue traveller's cheques?

5. Which fictional detective was created by Chester Gould?

6. Which footballer was voted PFA Young Player of the Year in 2000?

7. Who did the writer Robert Bolt describe as 'A man for all seasons'?

8. Who played Bert the sweep in *Mary Poppins*?

9. Which writer married Vivien Merchant and Lady Antonia Fraser?

10. Who was the first male singer to record UK chart hits on nine different record labels?

ANSWERS

1. HARRY Callaghan AKA Dirty HARRY 2. DICK Francis 3. Colonel TOM Parker 4. THOMAS Cook 5. DICK Tracy 6. HARRY Kewell 7. Sir THOMAS More 8. DICK Van Dyke 9. HAROLD Pinter 10. TOM Jones

FRUIT AND VEG

The answers to the following ten questions all contain the name of either a fruit or vegetable.

1. What is the wife of a Sultan called?
2. What is the capital city of Belgium?
3. On TV Fleegle, Bingo, Drooper and Snork were collectively known as who?
4. What is the nickname of Bournemouth Football Club?
5. What was the name of the character played by Angie Dickinson in the TV series *Police Woman*?
6. Which Beatles song was on the flip side of 'Penny Lane'?
7. Which character in the film *Toy Story* continually lost parts of his body?
8. Describe the vessel in which the Owl and the Pussycat went to sea.
9. Which South African state established by the Boers became a British colony after the Boer War?
10. What is the real name of the actor Howard Keel?

WHAT'S UP DOC!

The answers to the following ten questions all contain the word Doc or Doctor.

1. Whose home planet was called Gallifrey?
2. What is bingo slang for the number 9?
3. Who is the murder victim in the board game of Cluedo?
4. Who had a No 1 hit in 1986 with 'Spirit in the Sky'?
5. Who was arrested aboard the *SS Montrose* with his mistress Ethel Le Neve and was subsequently hanged in 1910 for the murder of his wife?
6. Which pop group's only UK Top 10 hit is entitled 'Milk and Alcohol'?
7. Sir Danvers Carew was murdered in which novel?
8. Who did Val Kilmer portray in the film *Tombstone*?
9. *Sylvia's Mother* was the first hit for which pop group?
10. In 1901 who became the first ever recipient of a Nobel Prize?

ANSWERS

1. Dr. Who 2. Doctor's Orders 3. Dr. Black 4. Dr. and the Medics 5. Dr. Crippen
6. Dr. Feelgood 7. Dr. Jekyll and Mr Hyde 8. Doc Holliday 9. Dr Hook
10. Dr. Emil Behring

IT'S THE SIZE THAT COUNTS!

The answers to the following ten questions all contain an adjective relating to size.

1. Who is the lead singer of M People?
2. In 1999 Michael J Fox provided the voice for which screen rodent?
3. Which pop group sang about whiskey in the jar?
4. What do the initials BFG stand for in the title of the Roald Dahl novel?
5. Which 1995 film set in Las Vegas co-starred John Travolta, Gene Hackman, Danny Devito and Rene Russo?
6. In the world of show business how are Cyril Mead and Edward McGuinness better known?
7. If Shirley Crabtree met Luke McMasters which two wrestlers would be in opposition?
8. Which classic film starred Humphrey Bogart as Philip Marlowe and Lauren Bacall as Vivien?
9. Who topped the singles charts in 1967 with the song 'Let The Heartaches Begin'?
10. What is the state capital of Arkansas?

COLOURS

The answers to the following ten questions all contain the name of a colour.

1. Which Gerry Anderson creation worked for an organisation called SPECTRUM?

2. Which sea did Moses part?

3. Ian Gillian and Dave Coverdale were both lead singers of which rock group?

4. Which man of the cloth is a murder suspect in Cluedo?

5. In which 1980 film were Brooke Shields and Christopher Atkins shipwrecked on a desert island?

6. Which book starred Alex DeLarge as a leader of a group of thugs?

7. Which is the oldest national park in America?

8. Who had hits with the songs 'Lonely Boy' and 'Never Let Her Slip Away'?

9. What is the title of the sixth novel in the Narnia Chronicles?

10. In 1999 what did Sunderland football club change its nickname to?

ANSWERS

1. Captain SCARLET 2. The RED Sea 3. Deep PURPLE 4. Reverend GREEN 5. The BLUE Lagoon 6. A Clockwise Orange 7. YELLOWstone National Park 8. Andrew GOLD 9. The SILVER Chair 10. The BLACK Cats

THE FOUR SEASONS

The answers to the following ten questions all contain the name of one of the seasons of the year.

1. In which film did Cliff Richard drive a red double-decker bus?

2. Where is the TV programme *Home and Away* set?

3. Which Shakespeare play features King Leontes of Sicilia?

4. Which song was a hit for the Kinks in the autumn of 1967?

5. Who played Bud Flanagan alongside Leslie Crowther's Chesney Allen in the stage production of *Underneath The Arches*?

6. Which song, taken from the album *The War of the Worlds*, was a hit for Justin Hayward?

7. What is the nickname of the South African Rugby Union team?

8. What is the full name of the vampire-slaying character played on TV by Sarah Michelle Gellar?

9. Who sang the first ever song to be performed on *Top of the Pops*?

10. How is Ladonna Andrea Gaines better known?

JOHN BOYS

The answers to the following ten questions all contain the name John.

1. Whose first film was called *The Drop Kick* and last film was called *The Shootist*?

2. Who was Britain's Foreign Secretary for just thirteen weeks in 1989?

3. Who was the last Englishman of the 20th century to be crowned World Professional Snooker Champion?

4. Who currently holds the record as Radio 1's longest-serving DJ?

5. Who was the first person to be dubbed America's public enemy No. 1?

6. Who was the cook aboard the *Hispaniola*?

7. Which convicted bank robber was played on film by Roger Daltrey in 1980?

8. Which ex-premiership footballer became Nigeria's minister for sport?

9. When mad cow disease first hit the headlines which Conservative MP was pictured in newscasts eating burgers with his children?

10. Who is credited with inventing logarithms?

ANSWERS

1. JOHN Wayne 2. JOHN Major 3. JOHN Parrott 4. JOHN Peel 5. JOHN Dillinger 6. Long JOHN Silver 7. JOHN McVicar 8. JOHN Fashanu 9. JOHN Selwyn Gummer 10. JOHN Napier

SOMETHING FISHY

The answers to the following ten question all contain the name of a fish.

1. What was the name of the character played by Ian Lavender in *Dad's Army?*

2. Which four-letter word is defined in the dictionary as 'to find fault, quibble, pick holes and whinge'?

3. Which Leicester City midfielder made his England international debut in 1999?

4. Which two-word name is a modern-day term for a usurer?

5. Which bearded seafaring character featured in Herge's *Adventures of Tin Tin?*

6. According to the nursery rhyme who could eat no fat?

7. Which pop group enjoyed hits in the 1980s with songs called 'Tom Hark' and 'Zambesi'?

8. Which male fashion accessory from the late 1960s was the invention of a certain Mr Fish?

9. Which former wrestler played the character of Bomber in *Auf Wiedersehen Pet?*

10. Which part of the body is stroked in order to test the Brabinski reflex?

ANSWERS
1. Private PIKE 2. CARP 3. Steve GUPPY 4. Loan SHARK 5. Captain HADDOCK 6. Jack SPRAT 7. The PIRANHAS 8. The KIPPER tie 9. Pat ROACH 10. SOLE of the foot

THE PLANETS SUITE

The answers to the following ten questions all contain the name of a planet.

1. What was the name of Mickey Mouse's dog?
2. Under what name did David Bowie and his backing band tour the UK in 1972?
3. Who drove Gerry Anderson's Supercar?
4. Which 1980 film co-starred Kirk Douglas and Farrah Fawcett battling against a murderous robot running amok on a remote space station?
5. Belinda Carlisle had a No. 1 hit in 1988 with which song?
6. What is the name of the Roman god of the sea?
7. Which is the first planet mentioned in the lyrics of the song 'Fly me to the Moon'?
8. Which horse won the Grand National in 1998?
9. In which 1996 film did Jack Nicholson play the President of the USA?
10. What was discovered by Dumond D'Urville on the island of Melos?

ANSWERS

1. PLUTO 2. Ziggy Stardust and the Spiders from MARS 3. Mike MERCURY 4. SATURN 3 5. 'Heaven Is A Place On EARTH'. 6. NEPTUNE 7. JUPITER 8. EARTH Summit 9. MARS Attacks 10. VENUS De Milo

HOT AND COLD

The answers to the following ten questions all contain an adjective referring to temperature.

1. Which character was played by Christopher Biggins in the sitcom *Porridge*?

2. Which villain did Arnold Schwarzenegger play in the film *Batman and Robin*?

3. Which Raymond Bradbury novel took its name from the temperature at which paper spontaneously combusts?

4. What was the name of the animated penguin created by Walter Lantz?

5. Which group had hits with 'Boogie Nights' and 'Always And Forever'?

6. In which film did John Candy play the coach of the Jamaican bobsleigh team?

7. What was the name of the controversial dance troupe that featured on Kenny Everett's TV show?

8. In which film did Tony Curtis and Jack Lemmon dress up as women?

9. Jenny, Karen, Rachel, Pete, Adam and David are the central characters in which award-winning TV series?

10. Who were voted Best British group at the 2001 Brit Awards?

ANSWERS
1. LUKEWARM 2. Mr FREEZE 3. FAHRENHEIT 451 4. CHILLY Willy 5. HEATWAVE 6. COOL Runnings 7. HOT Gossip 8. Some Like it HOT 9. COLD Feet 10. COLDplay

POLITICALLY CORRECT

The answers to the following ten questions all contain the surname of a British Prime Minister or American President.

1. Who did Denis Waterman play in *The Sweeney*?

2. What is the highest mountain in North America?

3. What is the real name of the author George Orwell?

4. On which race course is the Kentucky Derby run?

5. Which famous film star was arrested in a compromising position with a prostitute called Divine Brown?

6. Which founder member of the Beach Boys was buried at sea in 1983?

7. Who married Jennifer Aniston in the year 2000?

8. Who played Malcolm X in a 1992 film?

9. Which British city was founded by the Romans in 48AD to command the crossing of Ermine Street and Fosse Way?

10. Which actor played an amorous priest in the TV mini series *The Thorn Birds*?

ANSWERS

1. George CARTER 2. Mount McKINLEY 3. Eric BLAIR 4. CHURCHILL Downs 5. Hugh GRANT 6. Dennis WILSON 7. Brad PITT 8. Denzel WASHINGTON 9. LINCOLN 10. Richard CHAMBERLAIN

DOWN BY THE RIVER SIDE

The answers to the following ten questions all contain the name of a river.

1. Which actress played Gregory's Girl?
2. Who is the smallest of the Teletubbies?
3. Which chart-topping singer's real name was Charles Westover?
4. Parker and Barrow were the surnames of which infamous duo?
5. Which author recounted his life as a tramp in the novel *Down And Out In Paris And London*?
6. In which film did Jack Nicholson slit the throat of Marlon Brando?
7. Who was the manager of the 1972 FA Cup winners?
8. Who is the wife of the composer Tony Hatch?
9. What is the title of the film which was a sequel to *Romancing the Stone*?
10. In *Blake's Seven* which character was played by Paul Darrow?

ANSWERS

1. DEE Hepburn 2. PO (the longest river in Italy) 3. Del SHANNON 4. Bonnie & CLYDE 5. George ORWELL 6. *The MISSOURI Breaks* 7. DON Revie 8. Jackie TRENT 9. *The Jewel of the NILE* 10. AVON

THE STATE OF THINGS

The answers to the following ten questions all contain the name of an American state.

1. Which song opens with the line 'All the leaves are brown'?

2. Where do Manchester City FC play their home matches?

3. Sharleen Spiteri is the lead singer of which pop group?

4. In every episode of which TV series did we hear the line 'Book 'em Danno'?

5. What was the theme song for the Harlem Globetrotters?

6. Which song provided a No. 1 hit for the Dutch group Pussycat in 1976?

7. Who won the Women's Singles title at Wimbledon in 1977?

8. Which fast-food chain was founded by Colonel Sanders?

9. According to the Bee Gees where did 'the lights all go down'?

10. Which breed of chicken was named after the smallest state in the USA?

ANSWERS

1. CALIFORNIA Dreaming', 2. MAINE Road 3. TEXAS 4. HAWAII 5 – 0 5. Sweet GEORGIA Brown' 6. MISSISSIPPI 7. VIRGINIA Wade 8. KENTUCKY Fried Chicken 9. MASSACHUSETTS 10. RHODE ISLAND Red

A CALL TO ARMS

The answers to the following ten questions all contain the name of a type of weapon.

1. Which 1988 western film featured a gang called the Regulators?
2. To be a true Cockney what are you supposed to be born within the sound of?
3. Which H Rider Haggard novel features the character Allan Quartermain?
4. Which portly detective was played on TV by William Conrad?
5. Who topped the charts all over the world in 1999 with the song 'Baby One More Time'?
6. Which musical featured the song 'Anything You Can Do, I Can Do Better'?
7. Whose 1997 version of 'God Save The Queen' was banned by the BBC?
8. What is the name of the villain in *The Threepenny Opera*?
9. What was the capital of England before London?
10. Which Disney animation told the legend of the young King Arthur?

ANSWERS

1. *Young GUNS* 2. BOW Bells 3. *King Solomon's MINES* 4. Frank CANNON 5. Britney SPEARS 6. *Annie Get Your GUN* 7. The Sex PISTOLS 8. Mack the KNIFE 9. WINCHESTER 10. *The SWORD in the Stone*

FROM HEAD TO TOE

The answers to the following ten questions all contain the names of parts of the body.

1. Which pop group sang about 'The Road To Nowhere'?

2. Which Peter Benchley novel became a Steven Spielberg film?

3. What name was given to the final battle fought between the US Cavalry and the North American Indians?

4. In motorcycle manufacturing, what do the initials BSA stand for?

5. What was the nickname of *Star Trek*'s Dr McCoy?

6. Who on TV played a Geordie detective, on film played a moron from outer space and had a No. 1 hit with the song 'Ain't No Doubt'?

7. On a Monopoly board, which square separates Whitechapel and Old Kent Road?

8. Which horse measurement is equivalent to 4 inches?

9. Which British building is nicknamed Paddy's Wigwam?

10. What do Americans call the game of noughts and crosses?

ANSWERS

1. Talking HEADS 2. JAWS 3. The Battle of Wounded KNEE 4. Birmingham Small ARMS 5. BONES 6. Jimmy NAIL 7. Community CHEST 8. HAND 9. LIVERpool Cathedral 10. Tic Tac TOE

THE LETTER S

The answers to the following ten questions all begin with the letter S.

1. In Cockney rhyming slang what is a dicky dirt?
2. What name is given to the longest day of the year?
3. Which TV character's catchphrase was 'Magic our Maurice'?
4. Rudolph Hess was the last inmate of which prison?
5. In North America what is the alternative name for yeti or a bigfoot?
6. Which country is nicknamed the Switzerland of Africa?
7. William Styron wrote the novel and Meryl Streep starred in the film. What is its title?
8. Which horse won the Grand National in 1991?
9. Who was President Nixon's first Vice President?
10. What is the nickname of Walsall FC?

ANSWERS

1. Shirt 2. Summer solstice 3. Selwyn Froggit 4. Spandau 5. Sasquatch 6. Swaziland 7. Sophie's Choice 8. Seagram 9. Spiro Agnew 10. Saddlers

JIMMY RIDDLES

The answers to the following ten questions all contain the name Jim, Jimmy or James.

1. Who played the title role in *Carry On Columbus*?

2. In 1980 who became the youngest ever World Amateur Snooker Champion?

3. Who played the character of Bayleaf in TV's *London's Burning*?

4. Which character was played by Woody Allen in the 007 spoof *Casino Royale*?

5. Who is the only American President to be a bachelor?

6. Which American hero did Richard Widmark play in the film *The Alamo*?

7. What is the name of the trophy presented to the most valuable player in a single season of American football?

8. In 1972 who became the youngest ever singer to have a No. 1 hit in the UK?

9. Who connects the films *Misery*, *Rollerball* and *Alien Nation*?

10. Who wrote the novel *The Secret Life Of Walter Mitty*?

ANSWERS

1. JIM Dale 2. JIMMY White 3. JAMES Hazeldine 4. JIMMY Bond 5. JAMES Buchanan
6. JIM Bowie 7. The JIM Thorpe Trophy 8. Little JIMMY Osmond 9. JAMES Caan
10. JAMES Thurber

3

RANKS AND TITLES

The answers to the following ten pop music questions all contain a rank or title.

1. Who had a 1982 No. 1 hit with the song 'Happy Talk'?
2. Which former politician used to appear on stage in a coffin?
3. Which song was a 1965 No. 1 hit for Roger Miller?
4. Which group first charted in 1974 with the song 'Seven Seas of Rhye'?
5. What was the title of the first hit single for Dire Straits?
6. Waylon Jennings had a hit with which TV theme?
7. In 1969 which duo were performing the 'Harlem Shuffle'?
8. Which pop singer starred in the film *Purple Rain?*
9. Which group topped the charts with 'Mouldy Old Dough'?
10. Which famous album cover was designed by Peter Blake?

ANSWERS

1. CAPTAIN Sensible 2. Screaming LORD Sutch 3. 'KING of the Road' 4. QUEEN 5. 'SULTANS of Swing' 6. *The DUKES of Hazzard* 7. Bob and EARL 8. PRINCE 9. LIEUTENANT Pigeon 10. SERGEANT Pepper's Lonely Hearts Club Band

34

SIGN OF THE TIMES

The answers to the following ten questions all contain the name or symbol of a sign of the zodiac.

1. Who assists Jim Davidson on the game show *Big Break*?
2. Who wrote the novel *First Among Equals*?
3. Which singer first entered the charts with the song 'The Show Must Go On'?
4. What did Chris Evans buy for several million pounds in 1997?
5. What term is used in rowing to describe the oarsmen losing their rowing rhythm?
6. On TV who played Sybil Fawlty?
7. Which German rock group had a hit with the song 'Wind Of Change'?
8. What is the name of the principal mountain range in Turkey?
9. Which siblings assisted the cartoon character Tin Tin?
10. What is the connection between Diana Dors, Steve McQueen, Gary Cooper and Sammy Davis Jnr?

ANSWERS

1. John VIRGO 2. Jeffrey ARCHER 3. LEO Sayer 4. VIRGIN Radio 5. Catching a CRAB 6. Prunella SCALES 7. The SCORPIONS 8. TAURUS Mountains 9. Thompson TWINS 10. All died of CANCER

THE MONOPOLY BOARD

The answers to the following ten questions all contain an item or property found on a Monopoly board.

1. Who was the original presenter of *Question of Sport*?

2. In which area of London did Jack the Ripper commit his murders?

3. Who created the character Paddington Bear?

4. Which song topped the charts for Abba in February 1978?

5. Which was the first football club that Robert Maxwell was the chairman of?

6. 5-4-3-2-1 by Manfred Mann was the theme music for which 1960s TV pop show?

7. Which TV series featured the Ingall family of Walnut Grove?

8. What was Elvis Presley's first ever UK hit single?

9. 'You're never alone with a ....', was the advertising slogan used by which tobacco company?

10. Which song contains the line, 'Have you seen the old man in the closed-down market, kicking up the papers with his worn out shoes'?

ANSWERS

1. David VINE 2. WHITECHAPEL 3. Michael BOND 4. 'Take A CHANCE On Me' 5. OXFORD United 6. Ready, Steady, GO 7. Little HOUSE On The Prairie 8. 'Heartbreak HOTEL' 9. STRAND 10. 'STREETS OF LONDON.'

M PEOPLE

The answers to the following ten questions all contain a surname of a famous person beginning with the letter M.

1. In 1967 who is credited with inventing the synthesiser?
2. Which soap-opera character was shot in the chest on 1st March 2001?
3. Which pirate was knighted by Charles II and later became the Governor of Jamaica?
4. Which world leader was known as Il Duce?
5. What was the surname of the French brothers who established a famous tyre company in 1888?
6. Which famous soul singer died on Boxing Day 1999 aged 57?
7. Who was released from a prison on Robben Island in 1990?
8. Who was known as the Green Goddess?
9. Who composed the music for the film *The Good, The Bad and The Ugly*?
10. Whose tomb bears the inscription 'Workers of all lands unite'?

ANSWERS

1. Robert MOOG 2. Phil MITCHELL 3. Sir Henry MORGAN 4. Benito MUSSOLINI 5. MICHELIN 6. Curtis MAYFIELD 7. Nelson MANDELA 8. Diana MORAN 9. Ennio MORRICONE 10. Karl MARX

FILMS AROUND THE WORLD

The answers to the following ten film questions contain the name of a location or a nationality.

1. What was the title of the second James Bond film?
2. In which film did Jenny Agutter play a nurse who was treating a lycanthrope?
3. Which song, a No. 1 hit for Julie Covington was sung by Madonna in *Evita*?
4. Which film saw Jane Fonda investigating a cover-up at a nuclear power station?
5. What was the title of the 1976 western in which Clint Eastwood appeared for the first time alongside his future wife Sondra Locke?
6. In which film did Richard Dreyfus play an unconventional music teacher?
7. Which film based on a true story introduced us to the character of Popeye Doyle?
8. Which film starring Anthony Quinn in the title role was set on the island of Crete?
9. In which film did Michael Caine say 'You were only supposed to blow the bloody doors off'?
10. In which 1985 film did James Woods play a war correspondent?

CAN YOU DO IT!

The answers to the following ten questions all begin with the letters CAN.

1. Which TV programme created by Jonathan Routh played practical jokes on members of the general public and then asked them to smile?
2. What was the name of the train driven by Casey Jones?
3. What is the capital of Australia?
4. What word means to declare a person to be a Saint?
5. Which rock group had hits with 'Let's Work Together' and 'On The Road Again'?
6. Which twelve-letter word means bad-tempered?
7. Which series of stories was written by Geoffrey Chaucer?
8. What name is given to tubes of pasta stuffed with meat?
9. Which female singer hit the charts with the song 'Young Hearts Run Free'?
10. What name is given to the unit of measurement of luminous intensity?

ANSWERS

1. CANDID Camera 2. CANNONBALL Express 3. CANBERRA 4. CANONISE
5. CANNED Heat 6. CANTANKEROUS 7. CANTERBURY Tales 8. CANNELONI
9. CANDI Staton 10. CANDELA

READ ALL ABOUT IT

The answers to the following ten questions all contain the name of a newspaper, magazine or comic.

1. How was Diane Prince better known?

2. In the media what do the initials IBA stand for?

3. Which twelve-letter word is defined as 'a much-travelled person or someone without national prejudices'?

4. The Morlocks were a futuristic race that featured in which HG Wells novel?

5. What is the most expensive property on a Monopoly board?

6. Which horse won the Grand National in 1984?

7. Which film told the true story of Billy Hayes, who was imprisoned in a brutal Turkish jail?

8. A gnomon can be found in the centre of a what?

9. Whose autobiography is entitled *The Good, The Bad And The Bubbly*?

10. Which BBC comedy drama featured a singing group called the Teletones?

MONEY, MONEY, MONEY

The answers to the following ten questions all contain a word with a monetary connection.

1. What name was given to the wired, hooped underskirt worn by Victorian ladies?

2. Port Moresby is the capital of where?

3. Who was the first person to compere *Family Fortunes* on TV?

4. What name is given to a male rabbit?

5. According to the nursery rhyme who had 10,000 men?

6. In late 1999 who became the manager of the Welsh International football team?

7. Which show first featured the song 'Mack the Knife'?

8. What name is given to the most important position in an American football team?

9. David Van Day and Theresa Bazaar made up which pop duo?

10. Who did Philip Lowrie play in *Coronation Street*?

SINGING THE BLUES

The answers to the following ten pop music questions all contain the word blue or blues.

1. What was the name of Harold Melvin's backing group?

2. Which singer's biggest hit came in 1973 with the song 'Dancing On A Saturday Night'?

3. Which song topped the charts for Madonna in October 1986?

4. 'Don't Fear The Reaper' was a hit for which group?

5. Which song, a hit for Bobby Vinton, was also the title of a film directed by David Lynch?

6. Which song gave Crystal Gayle a Top 10 hit in 1977?

7. Eddie Cochran believed that there ain't no cure for what?

8. Which group had hits with 'Melting Pot' and 'Banner Man'?

9. What was the name of Georgie Fame's backing band?

10. Which two films starring Elvis Presley contained the word blue in the title?

ANSWERS

1. The BLUEnotes 2. Barry BLUE 3. 'True BLUE' 4. The BLUE Oyster Cult 5. 'BLUE Velvet' 6. 'Don't It Make My Brown Eyes BLUE' 7. 'Summertime BLUES' 8. BLUE Mink 9. BLUE Flames 10. *BLUE Hawaii* and *GI BLUES*

TAKING THE MICHAEL

The answers to the following ten questions all contain the name Michael.

1. Which famous cricketer had the initials MCC?
2. In March 2001 who was the best man at the wedding of Uri Geller?
3. On 16th May 1989 a group of people known as the Guardian Angels began patrolling the London Underground. Who sponsored this activity?
4. Who replaced Betty Boothroyd in the year 2000?
5. Who committed the murders in the film *Halloween*?
6. Which TV presenter's autobiography is entitled '*Polly Wants A Zebra*'?
7. Who wrote the novel *Jurassic Park*?
8. Which of the Goons died in 1996?
9. Which footballer's first win as a race-horse owner came in the year 2000 at Newbury with his horse Talk to Mojo?
10. Who played Detective Steve Keller in *The Streets of San Francisco*?

ANSWERS
1. MICHAEL Colin Cowdrey 2. MICHAEL Jackson 3. MICHAEL Winner 4. MICHAEL Martin 5. MICHAEL Myers 6. MICHAEL Aspel 7. MICHAEL Crichton 8. MICHAEL Bentine 9. MICHAEL Owen 10. MICHAEL Douglas

YOU WEAR IT WELL

The answers to the following ten questions all contain the name of an article of clothing.

1. What nickname was acquired by the Hollywood actress, Lana Turner?

2. With which song did Paul Young top the charts in 1983?

3. What is the name given to the fielding position in cricket which is the closest to behind the wicket?

4. Which stage show featured the song 'Close Every Door'?

5. Who was the manager of the 1986 European Cup Winners?

6. Aberystwyth lies in which bay?

7. Which Mel Brooks spoof film was set in Sherwood Forest?

8. The chemical product digitalis is obtained from which plant?

9. Which football club moved from the Baseball Ground to Pride Park?

10. St Helier is the capital of which island?

ANSWERS
1. The SWEATER girl 2. 'Wherever I Lay My HAT That's My Home' 3. SLIP 4. Joseph and the Technicolour Dream COAT 5. Matt BUSBY 6. CARDIGAN Bay 7. Robin HOOD, Men in TIGHTS 8. FoxGLOVE 9. DERBY County 10. JERSEY

44

MAN TO MAN

The answers to the following ten questions all begin with the letters MAN.

1. What word describes the crime of killing a person without malice?
2. Who wrote the book *It's All Over Now* following her divorce from Bill Wyman?
3. Which word for a type of fruit was once the name given to a Chinese official?
4. Which species of baboon is prevalent in West Africa?
5. What name is given to a person who takes care of hands and nails?
6. What word describes the power given to a person or a nation to act in the name of another?
7. What name is given to a political party's official announcement of their policies?
8. What is the medical name for the jaw bone?
9. Which pop group's first No. 1 was 'If You Tolerate This Your Children Will Be Next'?
10. Which film featured the song 'Nothing's Gonna Stop Us Now'?

ANSWERS

1. MANSLAUGHTER 2. MANDY Smith 3. MANDARIN 4. MANDRILL 5. MANICURIST 6. MANDATE 7. MANIFESTO 8. MANDIBLE 9. MANIC Street Preachers 10. MANNEQUIN

LIKE SISTER AND BROTHER

The answers to the following show business questions all contain the word sister or brother.

1. How were Bill Medley and Bobby Hatfield better known?
2. How were Joy, Babs and Teddy better known?
3. Which singing siblings were in the mood for dancing?
4. Who starred in the film *Duck Soup*?
5. The film *Devotion* told the life stories of which three woman?
6. Who had a No. I hit in 1992 with the song 'Stay'?
7. Which musical featured the song 'Bless Your Beautiful Hide'?
8. Which group appropriately sang 'We Are Family'?
9. What did Jack Dee win in March 2001 in aid of Comic Relief?
10. In which 1992 film did Whoopi Goldberg wear a wimple?

SMITH AND JONES

The answers to the following ten questions all contain the name Smith or Jones.

1. Which TV western recounted the adventures of a Hannibal Heyes and Kid Curry?

2. Who won the Ladies Singles title at Wimbledon in 1968?

3. Which MP once said 'If the fence is strong enough I'll sit on it'?

4. Which Dame was married to the actor Robert Stephens?

5. Who sang the TV theme for the *Love Boat*?

6. Who scored a headed goal for Liverpool in the 1977 European Cup Final?

7. Which actress, one of TV's original Charlie's Angels, went on to portray Jackie Onassis?

8. Who is David Cassidy's stepmother?

9. Which Henry Fielding novel became an Oscar-winning film adaptation in 1963?

10. Who is the leader of the A Team?

ANSWERS

1. *Alias SMITH and JONES* 2. Ann JONES 3. Cyril SMITH 4. Maggie SMITH 5. Jack JONES 6. Tommy SMITH 7. Jaclyn SMITH 8. Shirley JONES 9. *Tom JONES* 10. Hannibal SMITH

5

A ROUND OF DRINKS

The answers to the following ten questions all contain the name of a drink.

1. Which novel by Laurie Lee was set in Gloucestershire?
2. Errol Brown is the lead singer with which pop group?
3. In cycling what did the Tour of Britain change its name to?
4. What name is given to a horse's ankle?
5. In which village did Miss Marple live?
6. Alannah Myles had a No. 2 hit in 1990 with which song?
7. What colours are the home strips of West Ham United, Aston Villa and Burnley?
8. Which song first entered the charts for the Four Seasons in October 1962?
9. What was the name of the lead male character in the film *The Third Man*?
10. What is the capital city of Trinidad and Tobago?

STREETS AHEAD

The answers to the following ten questions all contain the word street.

1. Which nickname is given to the Bank of England?
2. Blanche Du Bois is the central character in which play by Tennessee Williams?
3. Where do Leicester City FC play their home matches?
4. In the Australian soap, where do the Neighbours live?
5. According to the TV ad what are made for sharing?
6. Which TV series featured the characters Renko, Joyce Davenport and Captain Furillo?
7. What was the name of the wrestler who in the 1970s grappled alongside Bobby Barnes in a tag team called the Hells Angels?
8. Where did Detective Mike Stone enforce law and order?
9. Which song, a No. 1 hit in 1958 for Vic Damone, featured in the film *My Fair Lady*?
10. Where did Oscar the Grouch live in a dustbin?

MUSIC TO MY EARS

The answers to the following ten questions all contain the name of a musical instrument.

1. How is the tympanic membrane better known?

2. Which newspaper was edited by Ken Barlow in *Coronation Street*?

3. Which record producer was a former member of the groups Yes and Buggles?

4. Scalene, isosceles and equilateral are all types of what?

5. Which famous scientist founded the *National Geographic* magazine?

6. Which song provided Ken Dodd with his first Top 10 hit single?

7. Rod Hull, Fred Trueman, David Bryant and Harold Wilson are all past recipients of which award?

8. 'No Matter What', a No.1 for Boyzone, featured in which stage musical?

9. Which American female vocalist had a 1965 hit with the song 'Rescue Me'?

10. Pamina and Papageno are both characters in which opera?

AMERICAN STATE CAPITALS

The answers to the following ten questions all contain the name of a state capital.

1. Which mythical bird is said to have risen from its own ashes?
2. Which astronaut became the Six Million Dollar Man?
3. Who wrote the song 'Take Me Home Country Roads'?
4. Which 1960s pop group had a hit with 'Tobacco Road'?
5. What is the French equivalent for the name of Peter?
6. Which superstar owned a pet snake called Muscles?
7. In the Bible who was the main writer of the Epistles?
8. Who sang the first ever song on *Top of the Pops*?
9. Who is credited with introducing potatoes to Britain?
10. Who was nicknamed 'The Iron Chancellor'?

ANSWERS

1. PHOENIX – state capital of Arizona 2. Steve AUSTIN – state capital of Texas 3. John DENVER – state capital of Colorado 4. NASHVILLE Teens – state capital of Tennessee 5. PIERRE – state capital of South Dakota 6. Michael JACKSON – state capital of Mississippi 7. ST PAUL – state capital of Minnesota 8. Dusty SPRINGFIELD – state capital of Illinois 9. Sir Walter RALEIGH – state capital of North Carolina 10. BISMARCK – state capital of North Dakota

CHESS GUESS!

The answers to the following ten questions all contain the name of pieces or phrases associated with the games of chess.

1. Fisher, Ramsey, Runcie and Carey have all held which position?
2. In which TV series did David Hasselhoff drive a car called KIT?
3. What sort of shop would you associate with the symbol of three metal balls?
4. Which song was a hit for the actor Bruce Willis in May 1987?
5. What is the collective name for a group of penguins?
6. The song 'Blackberry Way' was a No. 1 hit for which group in 1968?
7. What was the name of the yacht in which Ellen Macarthur sailed solo around the world in 2001?
8. Who died of cancer in 1994 and for many years presented the TV show *Record Breakers*?
9. What was the name of the backing group of Emile Ford?
10. What was the name of the debonair detective created by Manfred B Lee and Frederic Dannay?

ANSWERS
1. ArchBISHOP of Canterbury 2. KNIGHT Rider 3. PAWNbroker 4. 'Under the BOARDwalk' 5. ROOKery 6. The MOVE 7. KINGfisher 8. Roy CASTLE 9. The CHECKMATES 10. Ellery QUEEN

OH CAROL

The answers to the following ten questions all contain the name Carol or variations of it.

1. Who was the first woman ever to be seen on Channel 4?
2. Who was the song 'Oh Carol' written for?
3. What is the real name of Pope John Paul II?
4. Who is the lead singer with T'Pau?
5. Who directed the film musical Oliver?
6. Who was in London in 1948 and played Helen Herriot in *All Creatures Great and Small*?
7. Which newsreader who was born in 1944 went on to present a documentary series called *The Sharp End*?
8. What was the name of the little girl who appeared on the test card on British television throughout the 1960s and 1970s?
9. Who had a Top 10 hit with the song 'You're Moving Out Today'?
10. 'God bless us everyone', is the last line of which novel?

ANSWERS

1. CAROL Vorderman 2. CAROLE King 3. KAROL Wojtyla 4. CAROL Decker 5. CAROL Reed 6. CAROL Drinkwater 7. CAROL Barnes 8. CAROL Hersey 9. CAROLE Bayer Sager 10. *A Christmas CAROL*

ONE TO TEN

The answers to the following ten questions all contain a number commencing with one and ending with ten.

1. Katy Cropper was the first woman to win which TV competition?

2. Valentine and Proteus were the title characters in which Shakespeare play?

3. How were Steve Martin, Chevy Chase and Martin Short collectively known in the title of a film?

4. War, Death, Famine and Pestilence are the names of what?

5. Which novel featured the character of Billy Pilgrim?

6. In which 1958 film did Ingrid Bergman play the missionary Gladys Aylward?

7. Gluttony and pride are two of what?

8. Which 1960 film earned Elizabeth Taylor an Academy Award for her role as a prostitute?

9. The cast of which TV show had a hit album with 'Hedgehog Sandwich'?

10. Which group sang about the swords of a thousand men?

TREE TEASERS

The answers to the following ten questions all contain the name of a tree.

1. Rat, Toad, Mole and Badger are the central characters in which novel?

2. Which six-letter word is defined as neat and tidy?

3. What is the national symbol of Canada?

4. Which song did Laurel and Hardy sing in the film *Way Out West*?

5. What nickname is given to the city of New York?

6. Which spy did Michael Caine play in the film *Funeral in Berlin*?

7. Which song was a No. 1 hit for David Bowie in 1980?

8. Which film introduced us to the horrific character called Freddy Kruger?

9. Which Channel 4 soap opera is set in the city of Chester?

10. Cousin It, Uncle Fester and Morticia were all members of what?

ANSWERS

1. The Wind in the WILLOWS 2. SPRUCE 3. MAPLE leaf 4. 'The Trail of the Lonesome PINE' 5. Big APPLE 6. Harry PALMer 7. 'ASHES to ASHES' 8. Nightmare on ELM Street 9. HOLLYOAKS 10. The Addams FAMILY

OLD AND NEW

The answers to the following ten questions all contain the word old or new.

1. Little Nell is the central character in which novel?

2. Who collaborated with the England World Cup squad on their No. 1 hit 'World In Motion'?

3. What nickname is given to America's Stars and Stripes flag?

4. How are Purdy, Steed and Gambit collectively known?

5. What was the title of the children's story written by Prince Charles?

6. Marti Caine and Lenny Henry both won Grand Finals of which talent show?

7. What is the name of the famous geyser located in the Yellowstone National Park?

8. In which country would you find Mount Egmont?

9. What is the full title of the book on which Andrew Lloyd Webber based his stage play *Cats*?

10. Name the four American states that contain the word new in their name.

ANSWERS

1. *The OLD Curiosity Shop* 2. NEW Order 3. OLD Glory 4. The NEW Avengers 5. *The OLD Man of Lochnagar* 6. NEW Faces 7. OLD Faithful 8. NEW Zealand 9. OLD *Possum's Book Of Practical Cats* 10. NEW Jersey, NEW Mexico, NEW York and NEW Hampshire

56

PHIL AND DON

The answers to the following ten questions all contain the names Phil, Don or variations of them.

1. Who managed Leeds United, England and Saudi Arabia?
2. Who appeared on *Going Live* alongside Gordon the Gopher?
3. Who played the character of Crockett in *Miami Vice*?
4. Who was the first American driver to be crowned Formula One world champion?
5. Who duetted on the No. 1 hit 'Easy Lover'?
6. Who played the mysterious Dr Loomis in the film *Halloween*?
7. Who did the Queen's only daughter marry in 1973?
8. Who did Anthony Hopkins play in the film *Across The Lake*?
9. Which actor played Lofty in the sitcom *It Ain't Half Hot Mum*?
10. Which sporting world champion was found guilty by a Scottish court in March 2001 of assaulting two women?

ANSWERS

1. DON Revie 2. PHILLIP Schofield 3. DON Johnson 4. PHIL Hill 5. PHIL Collins and PHILLIP Bailey 6. DONALD Pleasance 7. Captain Mark PHILLIPS 8. DONALD Campbell 9. DON Estelle 10. PHIL Taylor.

ANIMAL MAGIC

The answers to the following ten questions all contain the name of an animal.

1. In which TV game show was Jim Bowen assisted by Tony Green?

2. Which singer had hits with the songs 'Morning Has Broken' and 'Moonshadow'?

3. What nickname is given to referees in American football?

4. What are you said to shed if you are pretending to be crying?

5. What is the title of the longest-running play in the history of the British theatre?

6. Which infamous duo stole bodies for Dr Knox?

7. Which character does David Duchovny play in the *X Files*?

8. Which song was a hit for Rolf Harris in the summer of 1960?

9. Who is credited with inventing the revolver?

10. What was the title of the controversial book written by golfer Mark James in the year 2000?

ANSWERS

1. BULLseye 2. CAT Stevens 3. ZEBRAS 4. CROCODILE tears 5. *The MOUSEtrap* 6. Burke and HARE 7. FOX Mulder 8. 'Tie Me KANGAROO Down Sport' 9. Samuel COLT 10. *Into The BEAR Pit*

DOWN ON THE FARM

The answers to the following ten questions all contain the name of something that you would find on a farm.

1. What name was given to the disastrous 1961 invasion of Cuba that forced John F Kennedy to issue a grovelling apology?

2. What is the symbol of Lloyds Bank?

3. What did my true love give to me on the 6th day of Christmas?

4. What is the name of the anarchic pop quiz show presented by Mark Lamarr?

5. What name is given to the small island at the southern tip of the Isle of Man?

6. What nickname was bestowed upon King George III?

7. Which song was a No. 1 hit for the Wurzels in 1976?

8. What is the nickname of Bradford FC?

9. Which glove puppet was the partner of the ventriloquist Sheri Lewis?

10. Which Sherlock Holmes story was set on Dartmoor?

ANSWERS

1. Bay of PIGS 2. Black HORSE 3. Six geese a'laying 4. Never mind the BuzzCOCKS 5. CALF of Man 6. FARMER George 7. 'COMBINE HARVESTER' 8. The BANTAMS 9. LAMB Chop 10. The HOUND of the Baskervilles

BI WORDS

The answers to the following ten questions all begin with the letters BI.

1. What is the French word for library?
2. What is the alternative name for a whortleberry?
3. What is the name of the bear in the *Beano* comic?
4. What collective name is given to plants that flower once in two years?
5. Which aviator was a famous literary creation of Captain W E Johns?
6. What name is given to the crime of having two wives or husbands at the same time?
7. Which literary character created by Keith Waterhouse was played on film by Tom Courtenay?
8. What name is given to the muscles on the front of the upper part of the arm?
9. Which dish is made from the saliva of swiftlets?
10. In *Treasure Island* who received the black spot from Blind Pew?

OCCUPATIONAL HAZARDS

The answers to the following ten questions all contain the name of a job.

1. Which comedian's catchphrase was 'Just like that'?

2. How is Annie Mai Bullock better known in the world of pop music?

3. Which actress played Betty Turpin in *Coronation Street*?

4. Who patented the world's first sewing machine?

5. With what name was Marilyn Monroe born?

6. Who was the Foreign Secretary in Tony Blair's first cabinet?

7. Which playwright wrote *The Crucible*?

8. Which personality was known for his odd odes in the TV programme *That's Life*?

9. Which former England international footballer's biography was entitled 'Both Sides Of The Border'?

10. Which female singer died aged thirty-two on February 4th, 1983?

MUSICAL CHAIRS

The answers to the following ten questions all contain the name of a type of music.

1. In which sitcom does John Lithgow play a manic alien?
2. How is the fictional character of Eric Claudin better known?
3. The first line of which song is 'Half a pound of tuppenny rice'?
4. Which film was the first 'talkie'?
5. How are Jake and Elwood known in the title of a 1980 film?
6. 'Fields of Fire' was the first hit for which group in 1983?
7. What is the name of the first book of the New Testament?
8. What name is given to the elected part of the Isle of Man's government?
9. Which song is traditionally sung at England's rugby union international matches?
10. In which 1983 film did Michael Douglas play a judge presiding over a vigilante court?

SUPERMACS

The answers to the following questions all contain a Mac or a Mc.

1. Who killed Macbeth?

2. Whose autobiography is entitled '*The Avengers And Me*'?

3. Ray Kroc established which fast-food chain?

4. Which former sporting world champion was nicknamed 'The Clones Cyclone'?

5. On whose novels was the award-winning TV drama '*Cracker*' based?

6. Who was the first Labour Prime Minister of Great Britain?

7. Which group recorded the multi platinum album 'Rumours'?

8. On TV who played Dangerman and the Prisoner?

9. Which Prime Minister became Earl of Stockton?

10. In 1997 who was appointed head designer of the fashion house Chloe?

ANSWERS

1. MACDUFF 2. Patrick MACNEE 3. MCDONALDS 4. Barry McGUIGAN 5. Jimmy McGOVERN 6. Ramsay MACDONALD 7. Fleetwood MAC 8. Patrick McGOOHAN 9. Harold MACMILLAN 10. Stella McCARTNEY

TRAINS, BOATS AND PLANES

The answers to the following ten questions all contain the name of a mode of transport.

1. Which TV game show was presented by both Sarah Kennedy and Julian Pettifer?

2. Which Oscar-winning film told the true story of Eric Liddel and Harold Abrahams?

3. What nickname was bestowed upon Helen of Troy?

4. Who painted 'Sunflowers'?

5. Which Muppet Show character was the nephew of the person who owned the Muppet theatre?

6. What was the title of Nena's 1984 No. 1 hit?

7. Which film featured villains called the Blue Meanies?

8. Which book by Jerome K Jerome featured a dog called Montmorency?

9. Which song was a No. 2 hit for Elton John in 1972?

10. What was the name of Popeye's dog?

ANSWERS

1. *BUSman's Holiday* 2. *CHARIOTS of Fire* 3. The face that launched a thousand SHIPS 4. Vincent VAN Gogh 5. SCOOTER 6. '99 Red BALLOONS' 7. Yellow SUBMARINE 8. *Three Men In A BOAT* 9. 'ROCKET Man' 10. JEEP

TOOL TRIVIA

The answers to the following ten questions all contain the name of a tool.

1. What name is given to the cocktail consisting of vodka and fresh orange?
2. Which film featured Steve Martin as a commuter desperately trying to get home in time for Thanksgiving?
3. Which fictional character's girlfriend is called Becky Thatcher?
4. What name is given to the chalk rocks situated in the Solent off the coast of the Isle of Wight?
5. Which 1990 film directed by Tim Burton co-starred Alan Arkin, Winona Ryder and Johnny Depp?
6. Who had a No. 1 hit with 'Itsy Bitsy Teeny Weeny Yellow Polka Dot Bikini' under the name of Bombalurina?
7. Who played Steve McGarret in *Hawaii 5-0*?
8. Which duo topped the charts in 1994 with a cover version of 'Twist and Shout'?
9. Which TV puppet was voiced by Ivan Owen?
10. Which detective created by Micky Spillane was played on TV by Stacy Keach?

ANSWERS

1. SCREWDRIVER 2. PLANES, *Trains and Automobiles* 3. Tom SAWyer 4. The NEEDLES 5. *Edward SCISSORhands* 6. Timmy MALLETT 7. JACK Lord 8. Chaka Demus and PLIERS 9. Basil BRUSH 10. Mike HAMMER

MR AND MRS

The answers to the following questions all begin with the word Mr or Mrs.

1. Which Dickens character was continually 'Waiting for something to turn up'?

2. What spoof chat-show hostess is portrayed by Caroline Adherne?

3. Which children's character lives at 52, Festive Road?

4. In which 1993 film does Robin Williams dress up as a woman?

5. Which book characters were created by Roger Hargreaves?

6. Who with a 118-inch waist had a Christmas No 1 in 1993?

7. In which 1997 film did Judi Dench play Queen Victoria?

8. Which Japanese detective was created by John P Marquand?

9. Which Simon and Garfunkel hit record featured in the film *The Graduate*?

10. In 1997 the National Federation of the Blind asked the Disney film studios to halt production of which film because the main character was considered to be insulting towards the visually impaired?

ANSWERS

1. MR Micawber 2. MRS Merton 3. MR Bean 4. MRS Doubtfire 5. MR Men 6. MR Blobby 7. MRS Brown 8. MR Moto 9. 'MRS Robinson' 10. MR Magoo

JACKS OF ALL TRADES

The answers to the following ten questions all contain the name Jack.

1. Which boxer was nicknamed the Manassa Mauler?
2. Who played the title role in *Dixon of Dock Green*?
3. Which associate of the Kray twins was played off film by Tom Bell?
4. Which song did Clodagh Rogers sing for the UK in the Eurovision Song Contest?
5. On 8th November 2000, a memorial service for whom was held at Blackburn Cathedral?
6. Who played the lead villain in the films *Young Guns* and *Shane*?
7. Who assassinated Lee Harvey Oswald?
8. Which member of England's 1966 World Cup winning team went on to manage a country in the World Cup finals?
9. Who played the Artful Dodger in the musical *Oliver*?
10. How is the criminal Ilich Ramirez Sanchez better known?

ANSWERS

1. JACK Dempsey 2. JACK Warden 3. JACK the Hat McVitie 4. 'JACK in a Box'
5. JACK Walker 6. JACK Palance 7. JACK Ruby 8. JACK Charlton 9. JACK Wild
10. Carlos the JACKAL.

AROROUND THE HOUSE

The answers to the following ten questions all contain the name of an item found around the house.

1. Which female boxer is nicknamed 'The Fleetwood Assassin'?

2. Which song provided Buggles with a chart-topping single?

3. Which mountain overlooks the city of Cape Town?

4. Which opera features the characters Don Alfonso and Ferrando?

5. Which Led Zeppelin song was covered by the Far Corporation?

6. Which musical was based on the book *The Milkman and Other Stories*?

7. By what nickname was American footballer William Perry known?

8. In which city did a lady called Sally Lunn originally sell the tea cakes that now bear her name?

9. Which animated children's TV series features the characters, Tommy, Chucky, Angelica, Phil and Lil?

10. What is a male ferret called?

SO FAR SO GOOD

. . . .

The answers to the following ten questions all contain the word good.

1. Which sitcom featured the character Margot Leadbetter?

2. The King of Bohemia is the subject of which Christmas carol?

3. Which British horse-racing course hosts the Sussex Stakes?

4. In which film did Bob Hoskins play a gangland boss called Harold Shand?

5. Which novel was a sequel to 'Little Women'?

6. In the sitcom *Roseanne* who plays Dan Connor?

7. Who scored an equalising goal for Chelsea in the 1970 FA Cup Final replay?

8. In which film does Robin Williams play a disc jockey in the armed forces?

9. Which song contains the lines 'There's no love song finer, but how strange the change from major to minor'?

10. In the Shakespeare play 'A Midsummer Night's Dream' what is the alternative name of the character called Puck?

ANSWERS

1. The GOOD Life 2. GOOD King Wenceslas 3. GOODwood 4. The Long GOOD Friday 5. GOOD Wives 6. John GOODman 7. Peter OsGOOD 8. GOOD Morning Vietnam 9. 'Everytime We Say GOODbye' 10. Robin GOODfellow

AUTHOR, AUTHOR

The answers to the following ten questions all contain the surname of a famous writer.

1. Which murderer live at 10, Rillington Place?

2. Who partnered John McEnroe to win four Wimbledon doubles championships?

3. Who directed the film *Gladiator*?

4. On which river does the town of Ipswich stand?

5. What is the title of the sitcom that features Windsor Davies and Donald Sinden as rival antique dealers?

6. Who won a gold medal at the 1980 Olympics for the Men's 100 metres?

7. Who was the lead singer of the 1980s pop group Dead or Alive?

8. Which actress was born Shirley Schrift?

9. Who was the first British footballer to be transferred for one million pounds?

10. Which is the world's largest airport?

BEST OF BRITISH

The answers to the following ten questions all contain the name of a place in Great Britain.

1. Under what name did Superman work for the *Daily Planet*?
2. Which DJ played the first ever record on Radio One?
3. Who wrote the novel '*The Moon and Sixpence*'?
4. Who scored the fifth goal in the 1979 FA Cup Final?
5. How are Mrs Page and Mrs Ford otherwise known in the title of a Shakespeare play?
6. What is the more common name for magnesium sulphate?
7. What name was given to the attire worn by Robin Hood and his merry men?
8. Who plays Emily Bishop in *Coronation Street*?
9. Which famous pop singer was born David Cook?
10. Fanny Price is the heroine in which Jane Austen novel?

ANSWERS

1. Clark KENT 2. Tony BLACKBURN 3. SOMERSET Maugham 4. Alan SUNDERLAND 5. *The Merry Wives of* WINDSOR 6. EPSOM Salts 7. LINCOLN Green 8. Eileen DERBYSHIRE 9. David ESSEX 10. MANSFIELD Park

KID'S STUFF

The answers to the following ten questions all contain the name of a character from children's TV programmes and literature.

1. Which former lead singer of Slade was promoted to headmaster in the TV series *The Grimleys*?

2. Which singer topped the charts in 2001 with the song 'It Wasn't Me'?

3. Which salad containing walnuts was named after the hotel where it was first made?

4. Who compered the Miss World pageant in the year 2000?

5. What is the name of the longest river in Italy?

6. Which streetwise cop was played by Gene Hackman in the film *The French Connection*?

7. Which song was a hit for the Fun Loving Criminals in July 1997?

8. Who replaced Colin Baker as Dr Who?

9. Who married Soon Yi Previn in 1997?

10. In the novel *The Water Babies* what was the occupation of Tom, the central character?

ANSWERS

1. NODDY Holder 2. SHAGGY 3. WALDORF salad 4. JERRY Springer 5. River PO 6. POPEYE Doyle 7. 'SCOOBY Snacks' 8. SYLVESTER McCoy 9. WOODY Allen 10. Chimney SWEEP

BOXER BEAT

The answers to the following ten questions all contain the surname of a famous boxer.

1. Which British MP relinquished the title of Viscount Stansgate?
2. Which author first introduced us to the character of Humpty Dumpty?
3. What name is given to someone who makes barrels for a living?
4. Which TV duo were played by Michael Brandon and Glynis Barber?
5. Which famous literary character made his first appearance in a story called *A Study in Scarlet*?
6. Which daytime TV presenter famously 'popped out' of her dress whilst presenting an award with her husband Richard at the Comedy Awards?
7. Which motor cycle manufacturer made models called Atlas and Commando?
8. Which pop group named themselves after a character in the film *Barbarella*?
9. Which actress played a prostitute protected by Bob Hoskins in the film *Mona Lisa*?
10. How is hydrated magnesium silicate more commonly known?

ANSWERS
1. Tony BENN 2. LEWIS Carroll in *Alice Through The Looking Glass* 3. COOPER 4. DEMPSEY and Makepeace 5. Sherlock HOLMES 6. Judy FINNIGAN 7. NORTON 8. DURAN DURAN 9. Cathy TYSON 10. China CLAY

BUILDING BLOCKS

The answers to the following ten questions all contain the name of a building.

1. What name is given to the equine female equivalent of a sire?
2. Which Dickens novel featured a rag and bone man called Krook?
3. In 1965 who appeared in the film *Dr Who and the Daleks* and went on to present *Record Breakers* on TV?
4. Which football team is nicknamed the Eagles?
5. Which song opens with the line 'On a dark desert highway, cool wind in my hair'?
6. What was the name of the ventriloquist whose dummy was called Lenny the Lion?
7. Which duo charted with 'West End Girls'?
8. What was the title of the second film that featured the heroic Indiana Jones?
9. Where do Fulham FC play their home matches?
10. Which was the only black and white film to win the Best Film Oscar in the 1960s?

SUN, MOON AND STAR

The answers to the following ten questions all contain the words sun, moon or star.

1. What was the nickname of Louis XIV of France?
2. What name did the rock star Frank Zappa give to his daughter?
3. Which TV programme created the pop group Hearsay?
4. Which musical features the song 'I Don't Know How To Love Him'?
5. What nickname is given to inhabitants of Wiltshire?
6. CJ was the boss of Reggie Perrin in which company?
7. What did Opal Fruits change their name to?
8. Who did Kenny Jones replace in a famous rock group in 1979?
9. Which religious leader was jailed for tax evasion in 1982?
10. Chris De Burgh, Shirley Bassey, Nat King Cole, Alison Moyet, Marti Pellow, Bobby Darin and Freddie Mercury have all been past winners of what?

ANSWERS

1. The SUN King 2. MOON Unit 3. Pop STARS 4. Jesus Christ SuperSTAR 5. MOONrakers 6. SUNshine Desserts 7. STARburst 8. Keith MOON 9. The Reverend MOON 10. STARS In Their Eyes

SESSION 8

GREEN ISSUES

**The answers to the following ten questions all contain
the word green.**

1. Who is the arch-enemy of Dangermouse?

2. Which song opens with the lines 'The old home town looked the same as I stepped down from the train'?

3. Where does Postman Pat deliver the mail?

4. Who managed the England football team in the 1982 World Cup?

5. Which Richard Llewellyn novel tells the story of the Morgan family and is set in a Welsh pit village?

6. What word is the opposite of deciduous?

7. In which 1990 film does Gerard Depardieu fall in love with Andie Macdowell?

8. Name the famous novel written by L M Montgomery which is set on Prince Edward Island in Canada.

9. Which nine-letter word is defined as a person who knows very little and is easily taken in?

10. In 1997 which American football team won their first Superbowl in twenty-nine years?

GOLDEN GRAHAMS

The answers to the following ten questions all contain the name Graham.

1. Who played the title role in the film *The Life of Brian*?

2. Which former England manager did the *Sun* newspaper depict as a turnip-head?

3. Who along with Lyn Paul was a female vocalist in the New Seekers?

4. Who was known as the Galloping Gourmet?

5. Which former Lancashire and England batsman wrote an autobiography entitled *Fox on the Run*?

6. Who wrote the novel *The Wind in the Willows*?

7. Whose backing group was called the Rumour?

8. Who was sacked as manager of Tottenham Hotspur in March 2001?

9. Which member of the Goodies was a qualified doctor?

10. In the 1984 FA Cup final which footballer opened the scoring for Everton?

ANSWERS
1. GRAHAM Chapman 2. GRAHAM Taylor 3. Eve GRAHAM 4. GRAHAM Kerr 5. GRAEME Fowler 6. Kenneth GRAHAME 7. GRAHAM Parker 8. George GRAHAM 9. GRAEME Garden 10. GRAEME Sharp

GAME FOR A LAUGH

The answers to the following ten questions all contain the name of a game or a sport.

1. At which school was the novel *Tom Brown's Schooldays* set?
2. Which stage musical featured the song 'One Night In Bangkok'?
3. Which Venetian traveller famously visited the court of Kubla Khan?
4. What was the title of the fifth film in which Clint Eastwood played the character of Dirty Harry?
5. In the business world what name is given to a market that is dominated by one company?
6. Which Disney character sang the song 'When You Wish Upon a Star'?
7. Under what pseudonym did Eric Clapton record the song 'Layla'?
8. In the armed forces what name is given to a floating bridge?
9. In which film did Laurence Olivier ask Dustin Hoffman 'Is it Safe'?
10. Rita Ray was the female member of which pop group?

ANSWERS
1. RUGBY 2. CHESS 3. Marco POLO 4. *The Dead POOL* 5. MONOPOLY 6. Jiminy CRICKET 7. Derek and the DOMINOES 8. PONTOON 9. *MARATHON Man* 10. The DARTS

10BC

The answers to the following ten questions all have names
with the initials BC.

1. Who appeared on TV alongside Larry the Loafer?

2. Which singer left the Go-Gos to forge a solo career?

3. Who claimed that he did not have sexual relations with
   Monica Lewinsky?

4. Who scored two goals in the 1968 European Cup Final?

5. In *Coronation Street* who plays Liz McDonald?

6. Who merited an entry in the *Guinness Book of Records* in 1983
   for writing twenty-six novels in one year?

7. In the world of show business who is known as 'The Big Yin'?

8. Who did John Forsythe play in the glitzy American soap
   opera *Dynasty*?

9. Who coached Torvill and Dean to an Olympic gold medal?

10. Who was the first ever actor to play Hannibal Lecter on film?

BREAKFAST TIME

··

The answers to the following ten questions all contain something you would eat for breakfast.

1. Who played 006 in the James Bond film *Goldeneye*?

2. What is the title of the only hit single for the Street Band?

3. How did Agrippina kill her husband Emperor Claudius?

4. Which 1991 film, set at a cafe, co-starred Kathy Bates and Jessica Tandy?

5. In which British sitcom did the central family own a pet called Mongo?

6. Who was the first Scottish group to have a No. 1 hit single in the UK?

7. What was the name of the kung fu heroine created by the Goodies?

8. The actor who played Templeton 'Face' Peck in the A Team took his stage name from which dish on a restaurant menu?

9. Which song was a Top 5 hit for Tori Amos in 1994?

10. Which TV presenter was sacked from *Blue Peter* for cocaine abuse?

ANSWERS

1. Sean BEAN 2. 'TOAST' 3. She poisoned him with MUSHROOMS 4. FRIED GREEN TOMATOES At the Whistle Stop Café 5. BREAD 6. MARMALADE 7. BLACK PUDDING Bertha 8. EGGS benedict – his name is Dirk Benedict 9. 'CORNFLAKE Girl' 10. Richard BACON

FIRST TO LAST

The answers to the following ten questions all contain a numerical position starting with first and ending with last.

1. What was the name of the pop group formed by Kenny Rogers in 1967?

2. In which award-winning sitcom does John Lithgow play an eccentric alien?

3. What was the title of the 1987 film starring Michael Caine, which was adapted from a Frederick Forsyth novel?

4. In an American court of law what does a witness 'take' if he or she wishes to remain silent?

5. In which 1999 film does Haley Joel Osment say 'I see dead people'?

6. Which Shakespeare play features the character Sir Toby Belch?

7. In which series of slash horror movies are the killings committed by Jason?

8. What name do golfers give to the bar on a golf course?

9. What name is given to the border separating North and South Korea?

10. Which long-running TV programme is set in the village of Holmfirth?

ANSWERS

1. The FIRST Edition 2. THIRD Rock from the Sun 3. The FOURTH Protocol 4. The FIFTH Amendment 5. The SIXTH Sense 6. TWELFTH Night 7. Friday the THIRTEENTH 8. The NINETEENTH Hole 9. The 38th Parallel 10. LAST of the Summer Wine

SAINTS ALIVE

The answers to the following ten questions all contain the word Saint or St.

1. Which Russian city stands on the River Neva?
2. Which building contains a tomb bearing the inscription *Lector, sic monumentum requiris, circumpice*, which translates as 'Reader, if thou seekest his monument look around'?
3. Melanie, Shaznay, Nicole and Nathalie are collectively known as who?
4. Who played the Bond girl Tiffany Case in the film *Diamonds Are Forever*?
5. Which school was created by Ronald Searle?
6. How is March 17th otherwise known?
7. Who scored a goal in the 1965 FA Cup Final and went on to form a TV double act with Jimmy Greaves?
8. Who had a hit record with the theme from *Soldier Blue*?
9. What is the alternative name for Westminster Abbey?
10. What is the capital of the island of Grenada?

ANSWERS
1. ST Petersburg 2. ST Paul's Cathedral 3. All SAINTS 4. Jill ST John 5. ST Trinians 6. ST Patrick's Day 7. Ian ST John 8. Buffy SAINTE Marie 9. The Collegiate Church of ST Peter 10. ST George's

BY GEORGE

The answers to the following ten questions all contain the name George.

1. Who became the 43rd president of the United States?

2. Who founded a film company called Handmade Films?

3. Who founded the Next fashion chain?

4. Which Tarzan-like character was played by Brendan Fraser in a 1997 film?

5. On TV who played Dr Douglas Ross?

6. Who played James Bond in the film *On Her Majesty's Secret Service*?

7. Who led the defeated troops at the Battle of the Little Big Horn?

8. Who wrote *Animal Farm*?

9. In which building did Prince Edward marry Sophie Rhys Jones?

10. Who is the only man to have won a Nobel prize and an Oscar?

ANSWERS

1. GEORGE Bush Jnr 2. GEORGE Harrison 3. GEORGE Davis 4. GEORGE of the Jungle 5. GEORGE Clooney 6. GEORGE Lazenby 7. General GEORGE Custer 8. GEORGE Orwell 9. St GEORGE'S CHAPEL 10. GEORGE Bernard Shaw

WEIGHTS AND MEASURES

The answers to the following ten questions all contain the name of a unit of measurement.

1. Who discovered the theory of gravity?
2. Which No. I hit for Diana Ross was written by the Bee Gees?
3. Which character was played by Karl Malden in *The Streets of San Francisco*?
4. In which 1954 film did Kirk Douglas battle against a giant octopus?
5. Which trio topped the charts with the song 'When Will I See You Again'?
6. In which 1996 film did Jim Carrey play a TV engineer?
7. Who duetted with Sarah Brightman on the song 'Pie Jesu'?
8. Who became the leader of the Labour Party in 1980?
9. Which comedian is married to Dawn French?
10. In which 1992 film does Rebecca DeMornay play a psychotic nanny?

ANSWERS

1. Isaac NEWTON 2. 'CHAIN Reaction' 3. Mike STONE 4. 20,000 LEAGUES Under The Sea 5. The Three DEGREES 6. The CABLE Guy 7. Paul MILES-Kingston 8. Michael FOOT 9. Lenny HENRY 10. The HAND That Rocks The Cradle

OH GOD!

The answers to the following ten questions all contain the name of a mythological god or goddess.

1. Which is the largest planet in our solar system?

2. Who played Granny in the *Beverley Hillbillies*?

3. Which sports manufacturers were forced to apologise for their logo because it resembled the Arabic for Allah?

4. Who was Rocky Balboa's opponent in the first two Rocky films?

5. What is the name of Mr Spock's home planet?

6. In the Oxford and Cambridge boat race what is the name of the reserve crew for Oxford?

7. In which disaster film did Gene Hackman play a priest trying to save the passengers of an overturned ship?

8. Which was the first statue in London to be sculpted from aluminium?

9. The name of which actress is used in bingo slang for the number 44?

10. Which company sponsored the 1997 London Marathon?

ANSWERS

1. JUPITER – the king of the Roman gods 2. IRENE Ryan – the Greek goddess of peace 3. NIKE – the Greek goddess of victory 4. APOLLO Creed – the Greek god of poetry and music 5. VULCAN – the Roman god of fire 6. ISIS – the Egyptian goddess of motherhood 7. *The POSEIDON Adventure* – the Greek god of the sea 8. EROS – the Greek god of love 9. DIANA Dors – the Roman goddess of hunting 10. FLORA – the Roman goddess of flowers

CREEPY CRAWLIES

The answers to the following ten questions all contain the name of an insect.

1. Which Disney animated film featured a hero called Flik?

2. What did Stuart Goddard change his name to when he took up a singing career?

3. What was the name of the yacht in which Francis Chichester circumnavigated the globe?

4. What was the name of the character played by Michael J Fox in the *Back to the Future* films?

5. What is the nickname of Watford FC?

6. What did Master Po call the young Cain in the TV series *Kung Fu*?

7. Which is the only pop group to top the UK singles charts in the 1960s, 70s and 80s?

8. What model car was Herbie in the film *The Love Bug*?

9. In *Coronation Street* what is the name of Emily Bishop's nephew?

10. Which sporting projectile weighs between five and a half and five and three quarter ounces?

ANSWERS

1. A BUG's Life 2. Adam ANT 3. Gypsy MOTH 4. Marty McFLY 5. The HORNETS
6. GRASSHOPPER 7. The BEE Gees 8. Volkswagen BEETLE 9. SPIDER Nugent
10. A CRICKET Ball

DAVID DILEMMAS!

The answers to the following ten questions all contain the name David.

1. On TV who played the characters of Michael Knight and Mitch Buchannon?

2. Who won the British Grand Prix in the year 2000?

3. How is the duo of Charles Hodges and Charles Peacock better known?

4. Which serial killer was nicknamed the Son of Sma?

5. Which MP's political career floundered following his highly publicised affair with Antonia de Sancha?

6. On TV who was know as the Botanic Man?

7. Which radio disc jockey is nicknamed Diddy?

8. What is the name of the hero in the novel *Kidnapped*?

9. Which actor starred in the films *Around the World in Eighty Days*, *The Guns of Navarone* and *Paper Tiger*?

10. In March 2001 Jill Hinchcliffe gave birth to a four kilogram (six ounce) baby girl. Who was the 61-year-old father?

LET'S HEAR IT FOR THE GIRLS

The answers to the following ten questions all contain a girl's name.

1. What name is given to a female donkey?
2. What was the name of the flagship of Christopher Columbus?
3. Which Dickens novel features the character Tiny Tim?
4. What is the common name for the impatiens plant?
5. In which film did Madonna play Breathless Mahoney?
6. According to the song where can you see 'pretty nurses selling poppies from a tray'?
7. Who did Una Stubbs play in *Worzel Gummidge*?
8. Which horse provided jockey Greville Starkey with his only Epsom Derby winner?
9. Tony Orlando was the lead singer with which pop group?
10. In which 1970 film did Richard Burton play Henry VIII?

ANSWERS
1. JENNY 2. Santa MARIA 3. A Christmas CAROL 4. Busy LIZZY 5. Dick TRACY 6. 'PENNY Lane' 7. Aunt SALLY 8. SHIRLEY Heights 9. DAWN 10. ANNE of a Thousand Days

LETS HEAR IT FOR THE BOYS

The answers to the following ten questions all contain a boy's name.

1. What is the capital of the Caymen Islands?

2. Who owns an Abyssinian Tripehound called Gnasher?

3. Who topped the singles charts in 1992 with the song 'Would I Lie To You'?

4. In which 1989 film did Billy Crystal fall in love with Meg Ryan?

5. Which Dickens novel features a character called Mrs Sarah Gamp?

6. By what acronym is the Premium Bond selector known?

7. Which pop group featured the Fairbrass brothers?

8. What is the capital city of Guernsey?

9. What name is given to the American stage and theatre equivalent of an Oscar?

10. In which TV series does Caroline Quentin play Madelline Magellan?

ANSWERS
1. GEORGEtown 2. DENNIS the Menace 3. CHARLES and EDDIE 4. *When HARRY met Sally* 5. *MARTIN Chuzzlewit* 6. ERNIE 7. Right Said FRED 8. St PETER Port 9. TONY 10. *JONATHAN Creek*

ANYONE FOR TENNIS

The answers to the following ten questions all contain the surname of a famous tennis player.

1. Which country and western singer acquired the nickname of the Man in Black?

2. In September 1982 who was appointed President of the SDP?

3. Which screen monster lived on Skull Island?

4. Which alcoholic drink is distilled from pears?

5. In the 1960s TV western who played the Rifleman?

6. Which former British Prime Minister was nicknamed the Welsh Wizard?

7. What is the official name of the Old Bailey?

8. What is the state capital of Texas?

9. What was Mickey Mouse originally called?

10. In which American sitcom does Ted Danson play a doctor with a bad attitude?

ANSWERS

1. Johnny CASH 2. Shirley WILLIAMS 3. KING Kong 4. PERRY 5. Chuck CONNORS 6. David LLOYD George 7. The Central Criminal COURT 8. AUSTIN 9. MORTIMER Mouse 10. BECKER

AND HERE'S THE WEATHER

The answers to the following ten questions all contain a word that is associated with the weather.

1. What was the title of Margaret Mitchell's only novel?

2. What was the name of Tin Tin's dog?

3. Which children's TV show featured the characters Bungle, Zippy and George?

4. What is the nickname of Alex Higgins?

5. Which pop group had a hit with the song 'Boogie Nights'?

6. Which film saw George Clooney battling against the elements at sea?

7. Which song was at the top of the hit parade in the same month that England won football's World Cup?

8. Which character did Brian Wilde play in *Last Of The Summer Wine*?

9. Which pop group had hits with the songs 'Marvellous', 'Lucky You' and 'Sugar Coated Iceberg'?

10. Which character created by the author R D Wingfield became the subject of a popular TV crime series?

ANSWERS
1. *Gone with the* WIND 2. SNOWY 3. RAINBOW 4. HURRICANE 5. HEATWAVE 6. *Perfect* STORM 7. SUNNY Afternoon' 8. FOGGY 9. The LIGHTNING SEEDS 10. Jack FROST

THE A TEAM

The answers to the following ten questions all begin with the letter A.

1. Alphabetically which is the first American state?
2. Which vegatable has varieties called Jerusalem and Globe?
3. Who wrote *The Loneliness of the Long Distance Runner*?
4. From which breed of goat do we obtain mohair?
5. Which is the windiest continent?
6. Who wrote the book *Diana Her True Story*?
7. What is the birthstone for February?
8. What is the capital city of Ghana?
9. Where in the body would you find the talus bone?
10. Which are the first two animals to be listed in the *Oxford English Dictionary*?

ANSWERS
1.ALABAMA 2.ARTICHOKE 3.ALAN Sillitoe 4.ANGORA 5.ANTARTICA 6.ANDREW Morton 7.AMETHYST 8.ACCRA 9.ANKLE 10.AARDVARK and AARDWOLF

92

PROPER CHARLIES!

The answers to the following ten questions all contain the name Charles or Charlie.

1. Reputedly whose last words were 'Let not poor Nell starve'?
2. What was the name of the aristocratice dummy of the ventriloquist Ray Alan?
3. Who was the first French singer to have a No. 1 hit single in the UK?
4. Which jazz musician was nicknamed Bird?
5. Who married Oona O'Neill and Paulette Goddard?
6. Who starred in the films *Alien 3*, *The Golden Child* and *Last Action Hero*?
7. Who was known as the world's most perfectly developed man?
8. Which famous aviator's baby son was kidnapped and killed in 1932?
9. What is the name of the well-endowed female partner of Alan Titchmarsh on *Ground Force*?
10. Which entertainer was born Charles Springall?

ANSWERS

1. CHARLES II 2. Lord CHARLES 3. CHARLES Aznavour 4. CHARLIE Parker 5. CHARLIE Chaplin 6. CHARLES Dance 7. CHARLES Atlas 8. CHARLES Lindbergh 9. CHARLIE Dimmock 10. CHARLIE Drake

HAPPY ANNIVERSARY

The answers to the following ten questions all contain the name of a wedding anniversary.

1. The name of which singer is used in cockney rhyming slang for a curry?

2. Which opera by Bizet was set in Sri Lanka?

3. Which character was played by Suzie Quatro in the sitcom *Happy Days*?

4. Which singer had a hit with the song 'Don't It Make My Brown Eyes Blue'?

5. Who is the wife of Geoffrey Durham?

6. In which 1994 film did Glenn Close play the tyrannical boss of Michael Keaton?

7. In which 1970s TV series did Joanna Lumley communicate with David McCallum using the powers of ESP?

8. Which song provided a No1 hit for Stevie Wonder and Paul McCartney?

9. How was the screen villain called Scaramanger otherwise known?

10. What is the stage name of the singer who was born Noah Kaminsky?

THE END IS NIGH!

. . . .

The answers to the following ten questions all contain the letters END.

1. Which song that features in the musical *Sweet Charity* opens with the line, 'The minute you walked in the joint'?

2. Which mythical monster was slain by Beowulf?

3. What is the name of the chief ferry port in Belgium?

4. What was the full name of the young girl who accompanied Peter Pan to Never, Never Land?

5. Which long-running TV series, was created by Julia Smith and Tony Holland?

6. Who was elected MP for Hampstead and Highgate in 1992?

7. Who played the mother of Jane Horrocks in the film *Little Voice*?

8. Which song provided the Pet Shop Boys with their first chart topping single?

9. What name is given to the tissue surrounding a developing seed?

10. Which novel by Edgar Allan Poe was set during the Spanish Inquisition?

ANSWERS

1. 'Big SpENDer' 2. GrENDel 3. OstEND 4. WENDy Darling 5. *EastENDers* 6. GlENDa Jackson 7. BrENDa Blethyn 8. 'West END Girls' 9. ENDosperm 10. *The Pit and the PENDulum*